'An Artist Once Said'

By Hannah Rollings

LOM ART

ILLUSTRATED BY HANNAH ROLLINGS

ART EDITOR
LUCIENNE O'MARA

DESIGNED BY ZOE BRADLEY
COVER BY JOHN BIGWOOD

First published in Great Britain in 2015 by LOM ART, an imprint of
Michael O'Mara Books Limited, 9 Lion Yard, Tremadoc Road, London SW4 7NQ

W www.mombooks.com
f Michael O'Mara Books
  @OMaraBooks

Illustrations copyright © Hannah Rollings

A CIP catalogue record for this book is available from the British Library.

ISBN: 978-1-91055-201-8

2 4 6 8 10 9 7 5 3 1

Printed and bound in China

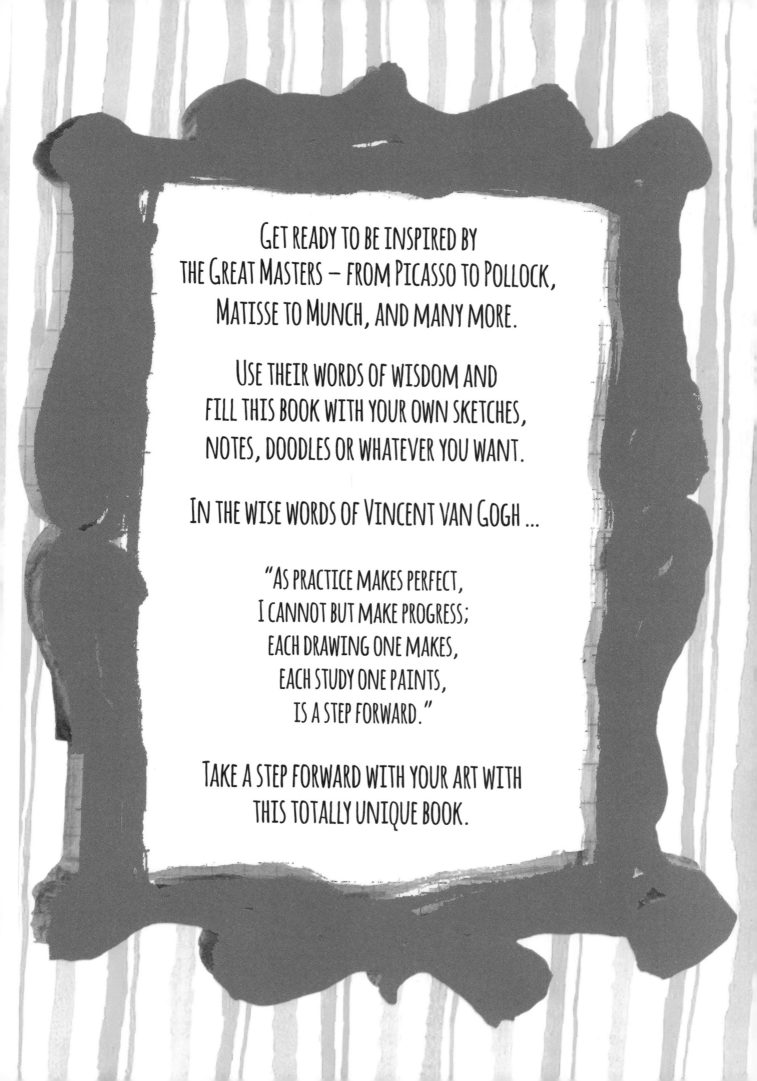

Get ready to be inspired by
the Great Masters – from Picasso to Pollock,
Matisse to Munch, and many more.

Use their words of wisdom and
fill this book with your own sketches,
notes, doodles or whatever you want.

In the wise words of Vincent van Gogh ...

"As practice makes perfect,
I cannot but make progress;
each drawing one makes,
each study one paints,
is a step forward."

Take a step forward with your art with
this totally unique book.

"I PAINt MYSELF BECAUSE ...

... I AM
tHE SUBJECT
I KNOW BEST."

FRIDA KAHLO

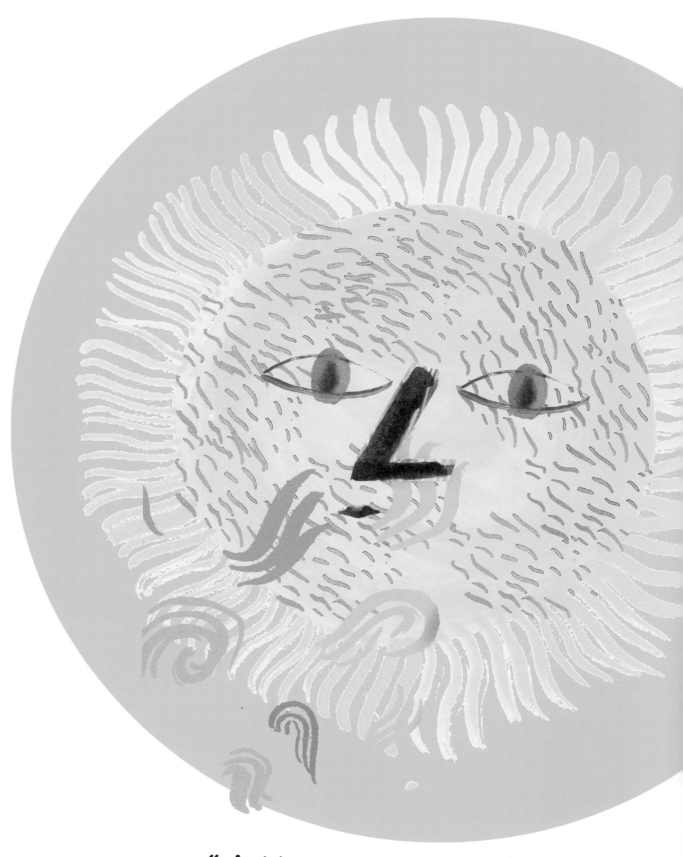

"YELLOW IS CAPABLE
OF CHARMING GOD."

VINCENT VAN GOGH

"THERE IS NOTHING MORE DIFFICULT FOR A TRULY CREATIVE PAINTER THAN TO PAINT A ROSE, BECAUSE BEFORE HE CAN DO SO HE HAS FIRST TO FORGET ALL THE ROSES THAT WERE EVER PAINTED."

HENRI MATISSE

"I GOT
HALF-A-DOZEN
PAINTINGS
FROM THAT
SHATTERED
PLATE."

GEORGIA
O'KEEFFE

"I like to **PRETEND** that my art has nothing to do with me."

ROY LICHTENSTEIN

"THE ARTIST DOES NOT
DRAW WHAT HE SEES ...

... BUT WHAT HE MUST
MAKE OTHERS SEE."
EDGAR DEGAS

"PAINTING IS JUST ANOTHER WAY OF KEEPING A DIARY." PABLO PICASSO

MONDAY

tUESDAY

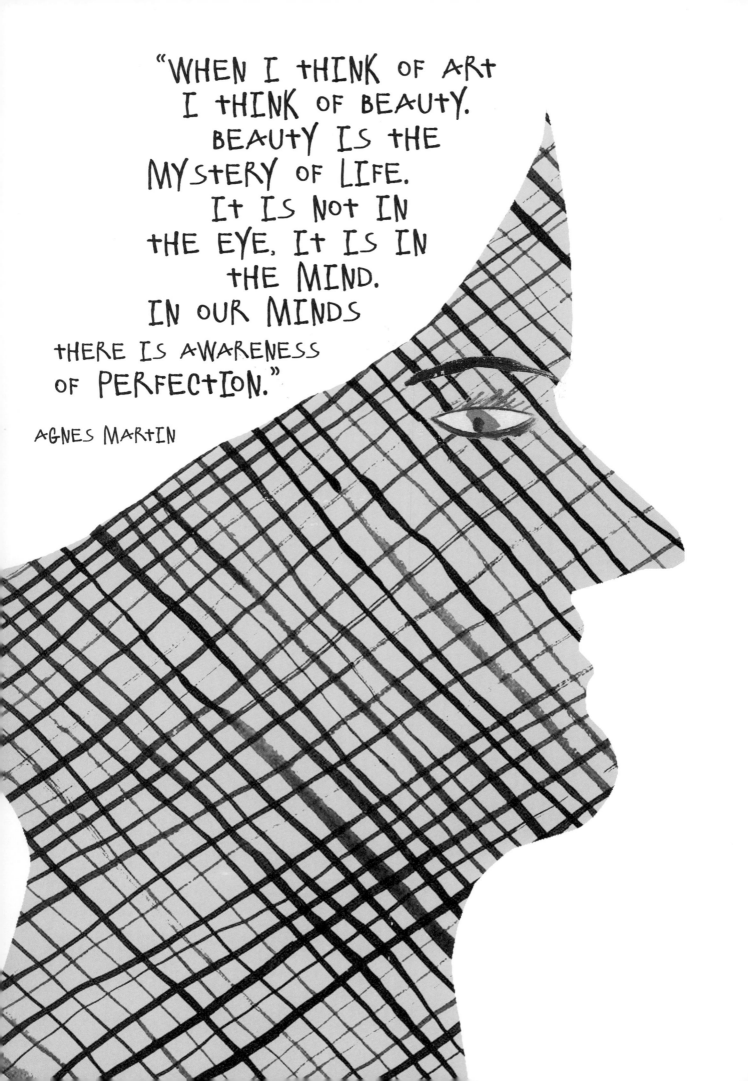

"WHEN I tHINK OF ARt
I tHINK OF BEAUtY.
BEAUtY IS tHE
MYStERY OF LIFE.
It IS NOt IN
tHE EYE, It IS IN
tHE MIND.
IN OUR MINDS
tHERE IS AWARENESS
OF PERFECtION."

AGNES MARtIN

"SEEK FOR THE BOLDEST COLOUR POSSIBLE, CONTENT IS IRRELEVANT."
HENRI MATISSE

"A PAINTING to ME
IS PRIMARILY A VERB,
NOT A NOUN —
AN **EVENT** FIRST
AND ONLY
SECONDARILY AN IMAGE."

ELAINE DE KOONING

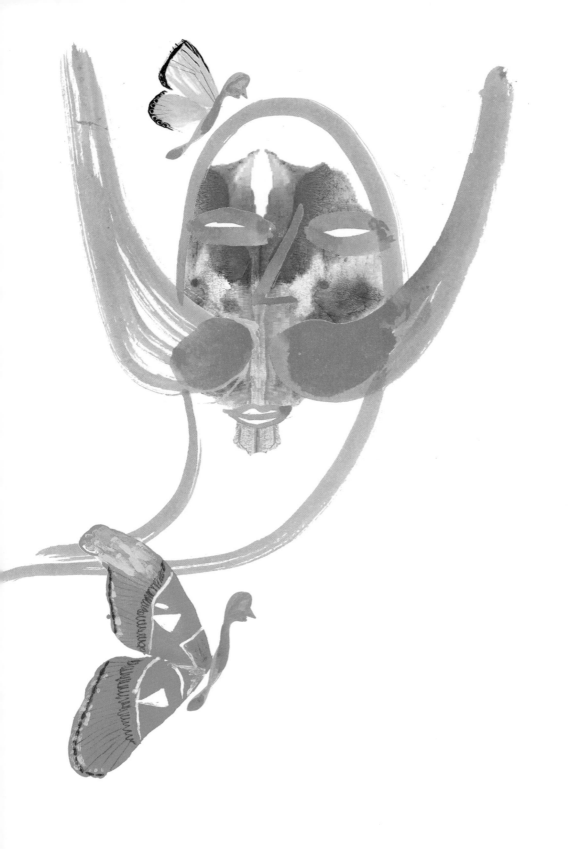

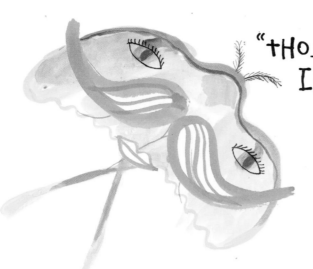

"tHOSE WHO DO NOt WANt to
IMItAtE ANYtHING,
PRODUCE NOtHING."

SALVADOR DALÍ

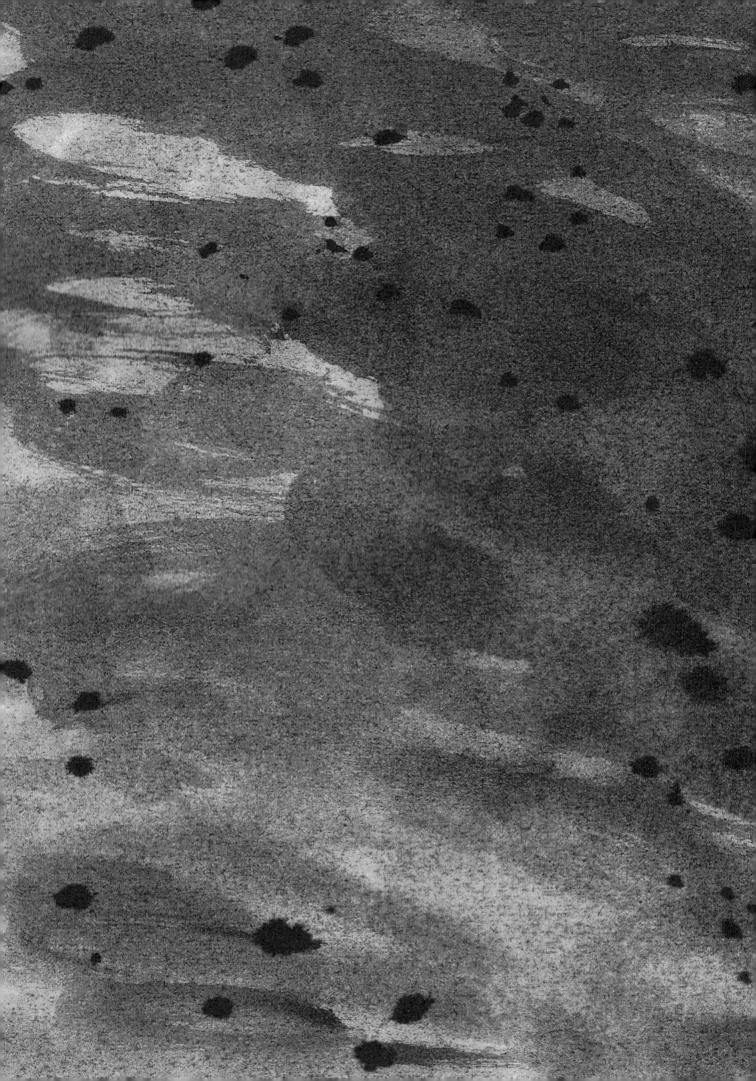

"A PAINTER SHOULD BEGIN EVERY CANVAS WITH A WASH OF BLACK, BECAUSE ALL THINGS IN NATURE ARE DARK EXCEPT WHERE EXPOSED BY THE LIGHT."

LEONARDO DA VINCI

"COVER THE CANVAS AT THE FIRST GO,
THEN WORK AT IT UNTIL YOU CAN SEE
NOTHING MORE TO ADD."
CAMILLE PISSARRO

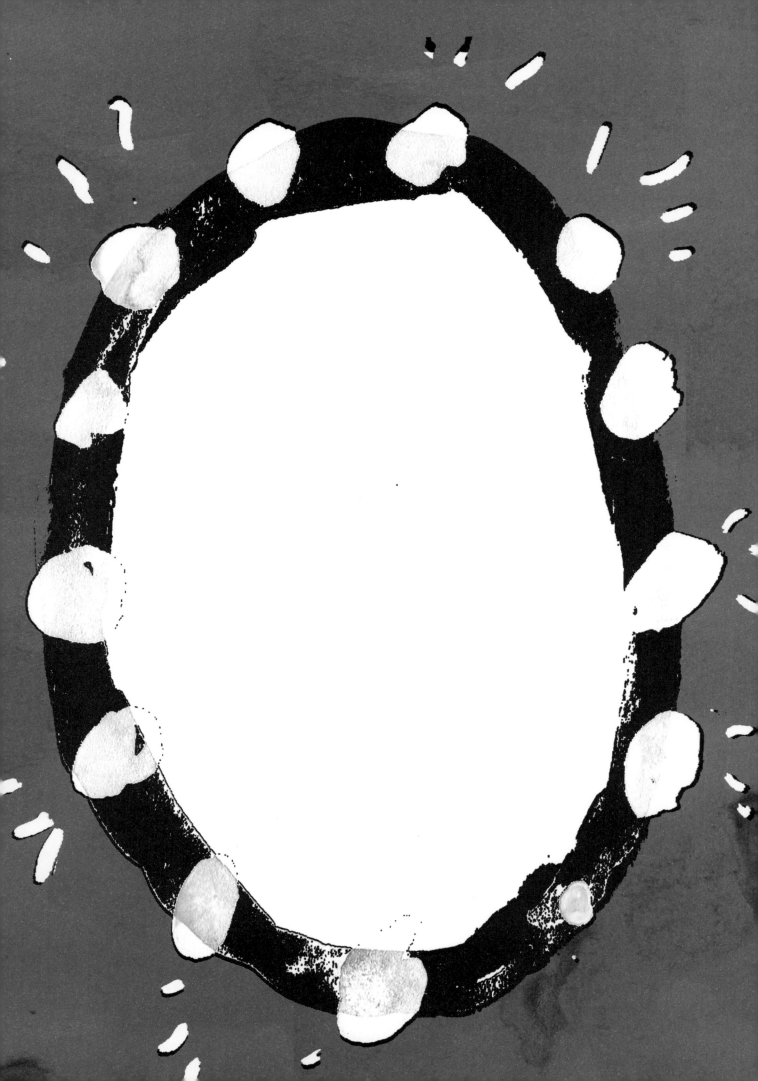

"MY IDEA OF A GOOD PICTURE
IS ONE THAT'S IN FOCUS
AND OF A FAMOUS PERSON."
ANDY WARHOL

"EVERYTHING
YOU CAN
IMAGINE
IS REAL."
PABLO PICASSO

"THE GREATER DANGER
FOR MOST OF US
LIES NOT IN SETTING
OUR AIM TOO HIGH
AND FALLING SHORT;
BUT IN SETTING
OUR AIM TOO LOW,
AND ACHIEVING
OUR MARK."

MICHELANGELO

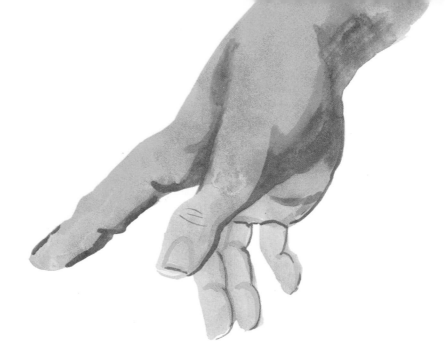

"I WOULDN'T MIND
TURNING INTO A
VERMILLION GOLDFISH ."

HENRI MATISSE

"WHY DO tWO COLOURS, PUt ONE NEXt to tHE OTHER, SING?"

PABLO PICASSO

"THE LONGER YOU LOOK AT AN OBJECT, THE MORE ABSTRACT IT BECOMES AND, IRONICALLY, THE MORE REAL."

LUCIAN FREUD

"to DRAW
YOU MUST
CLOSE
YOUR EYES
AND SING."

PABLO PICASSO

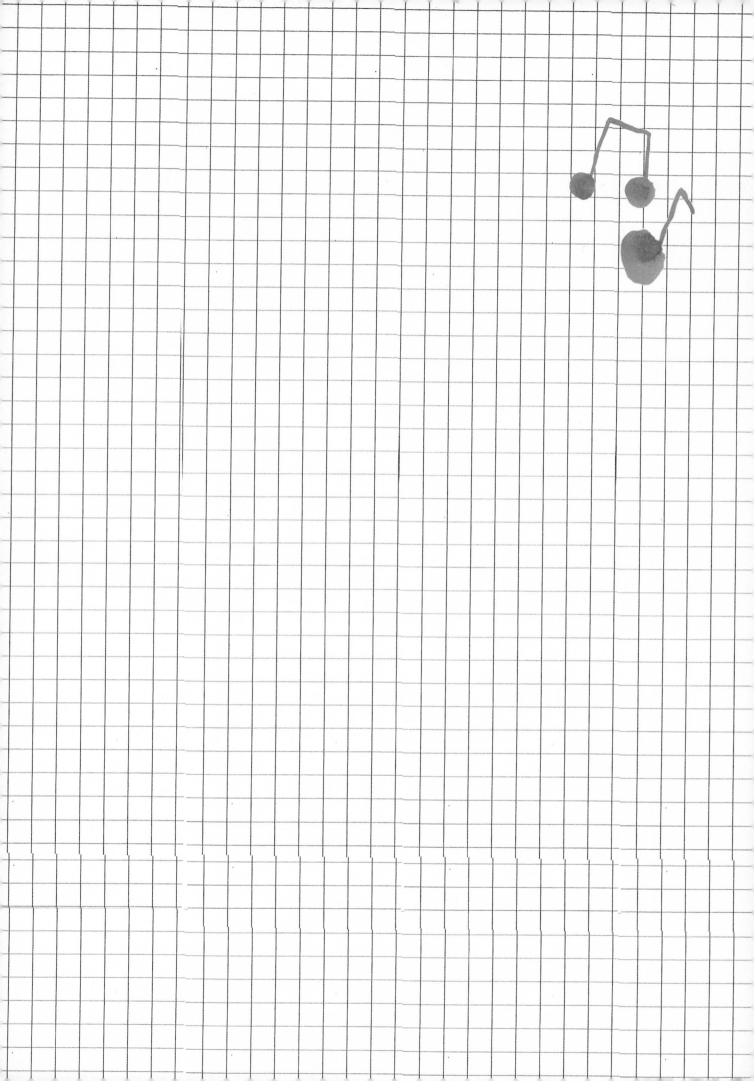

"I WILL
SOMETIMES
START A PICTURE
FEELING 'WHAT
WILL HAPPEN
IF I WORK WITH
THREE BLUES
AND ANOTHER COLOUR,
AND MAYBE MORE OR
LESS OF THE OTHER
COLOUR THAN THE
COMBINED BLUES?' "

HELEN FRANKENTHALER

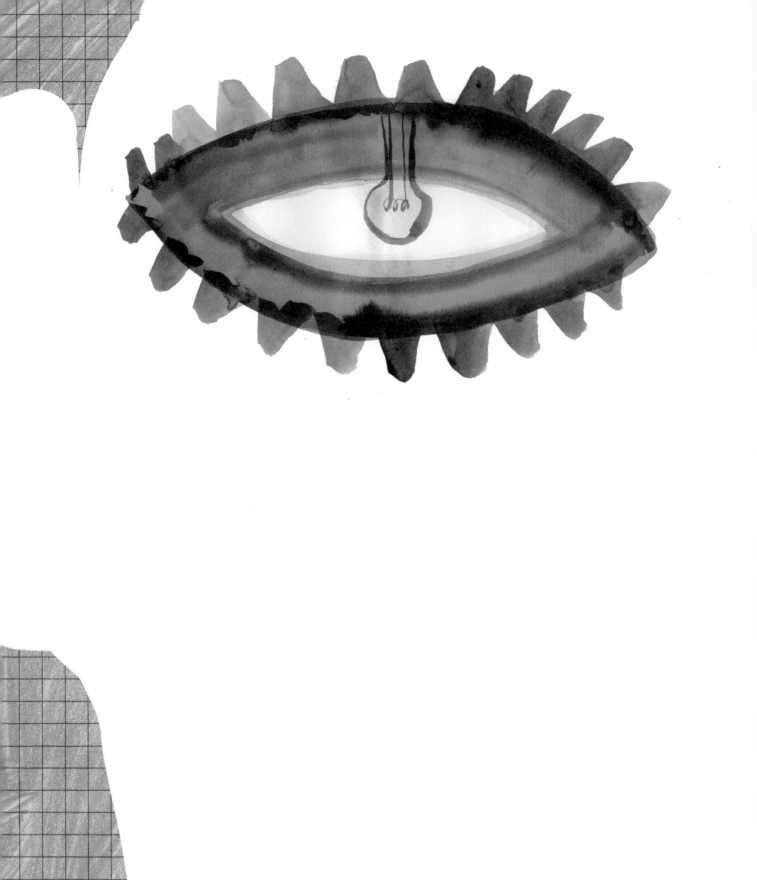

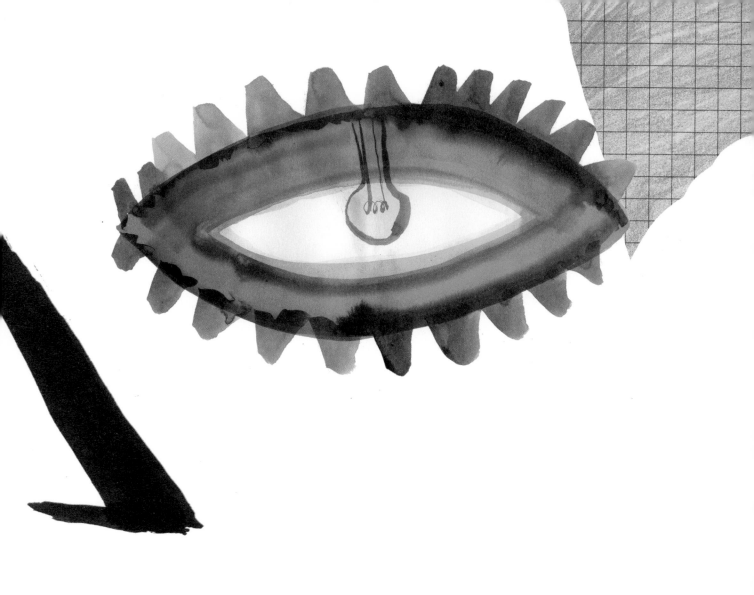

"EVERYTHING WE SEE
HIDES ANOTHER THING.
WE ALWAYS WANT TO SEE
WHAT IS HIDDEN
BY WHAT WE SEE."

RENÉ MAGRITTE

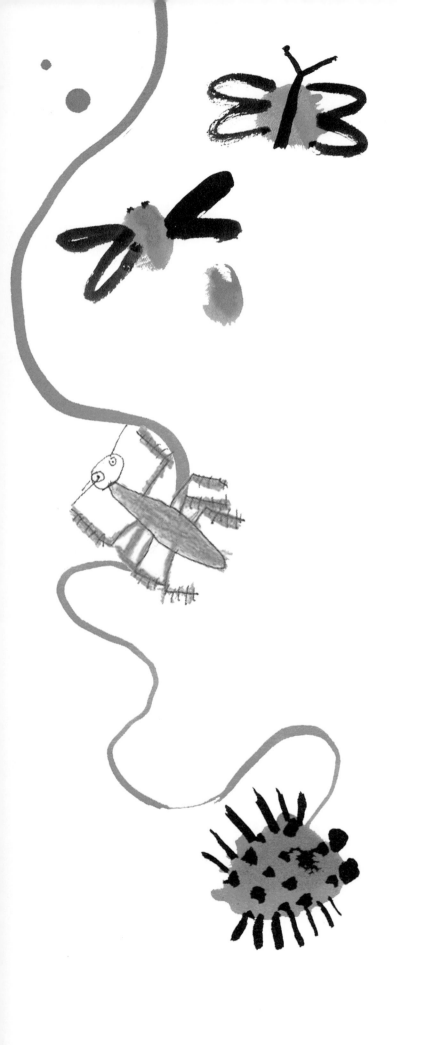

"ALL CHILDREN ARE ARTISTS.
THE PROBLEM IS HOW TO REMAIN AN ARTIST
ONCE HE GROWS UP."

PABLO PICASSO

"GREAT ART
PICKS UP
WHERE NATURE
ENDS."

MARC
CHAGALL

"A WORK OF ART
WHICH DID NOT BEGIN
IN EMOTION IS NOT ART."

PAUL CÉZANNE

"IN ART, THERE'S ONLY ONE THING THAT MATTERS: THAT WHICH CANNOT BE EXPLAINED."

GEORGES BRAQUE

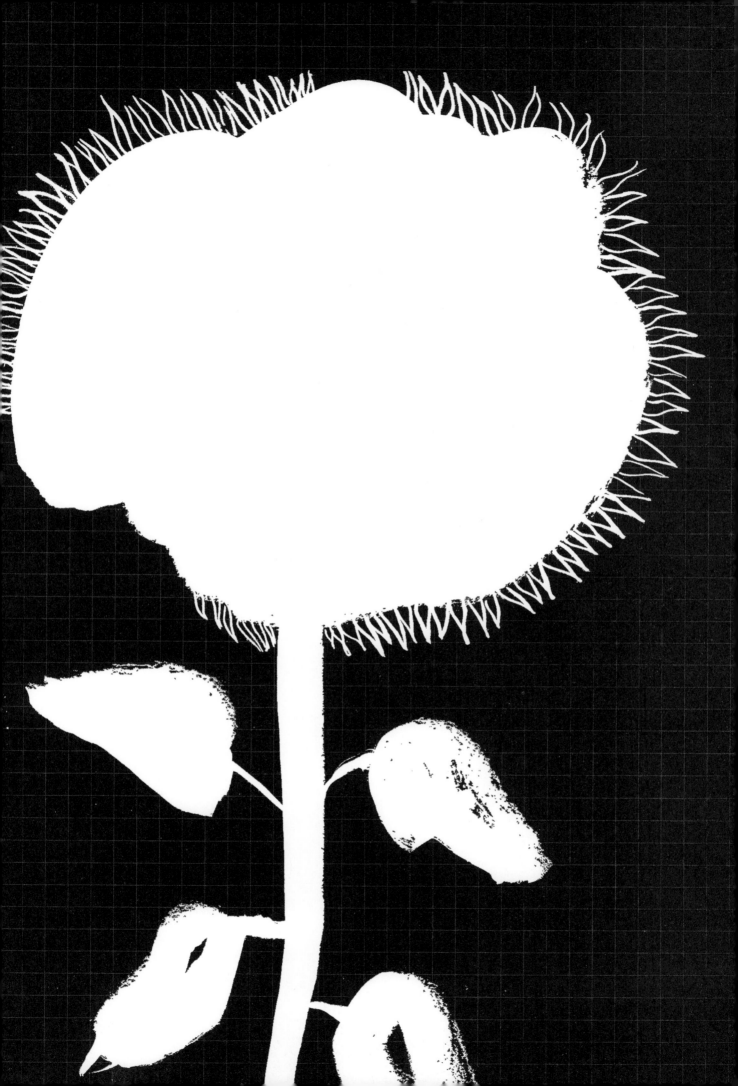

"I THINK THAT
A REALLY GOOD
PICTURE LOOKS AS IF
IT ALL HAPPENED
AT ONCE,
AN IMMEDIATE
IMAGE."
HELEN FRANKENTHALER

"SOME PAINTERS transform the SUN into a YELLOW SPOT; others TRANSFORM A YELLOW SPOT into THE SUN."

PABLO PICASSO

"A LINE IS A DOT
THAT WENT
FOR A WALK."
PAUL KLEE

"I DREAM MY PAINTING,
AND THEN I PAINT MY DREAM."
VINCENT VAN GOGH

"I AM AN ECLECTIC PAINTER BY CHANCE; I CAN OPEN ALMOST ANY BOOK OF REPRODUCTIONS AND FIND A PAINTING I COULD BE INFLUENCED BY."

WILLEM DE KOONING

"MY WORKS ARE AN IMITATION OF ...

... MY OWN PASt AND PRESENt."

BARBARA
HEPWORtH

"EVERY GOOD ARTIST PAINTS WHAT HE IS."

JACKSON POLLOCK

"I DON'T SAY EVERYTHING,
BUT I PAINT EVERYTHING."
PABLO PICASSO

"I'D ASKED AROUND 10 OR 15 PEOPLE FOR SUGGESTIONS. FINALLY ONE LADY FRIEND ASKED THE RIGHT QUESTION.

'WELL, WHAT DO YOU LOVE THE MOST?'

THAT'S HOW I STARTED PAINTING MONEY."

ANDY WARHOL

"I PAINT OBJECTS
AS I THINK THEM,
NOT AS I SEE THEM."
PABLO PICASSO

"I FOUND THAT
I COULD SAY THINGS
WITH COLOUR AND SHAPES
THAT I COULDN'T SAY
IN ANY OTHER WAY – THINGS
THAT I HAD NO WORDS FOR."

GEORGIA O'KEEFFE

"A PAINTING REQUIRES A LITTLE MYSTERY,
SOME VAGUENESS, SOME FANTASY.
WHEN YOU ALWAYS
MAKE YOUR MEANING PERFECTLY PLAIN
YOU END UP BORING PEOPLE."

EDGAR DEGAS

"COLOUR IS EVERYTHING, COLOUR IS VIBRATION LIKE MUSIC."

MARC CHAGALL

"THERE ARE ALWAYS FLOWERS FOR THOSE WHO WANT TO SEE THEM."

HENRI MATISSE

"ONE EYE SEES,

THE OTHER FEELS."

PAUL KLEE

"I WANT to PAINt
THE FEELING OF A SPACE."
JOAN MITCHELL

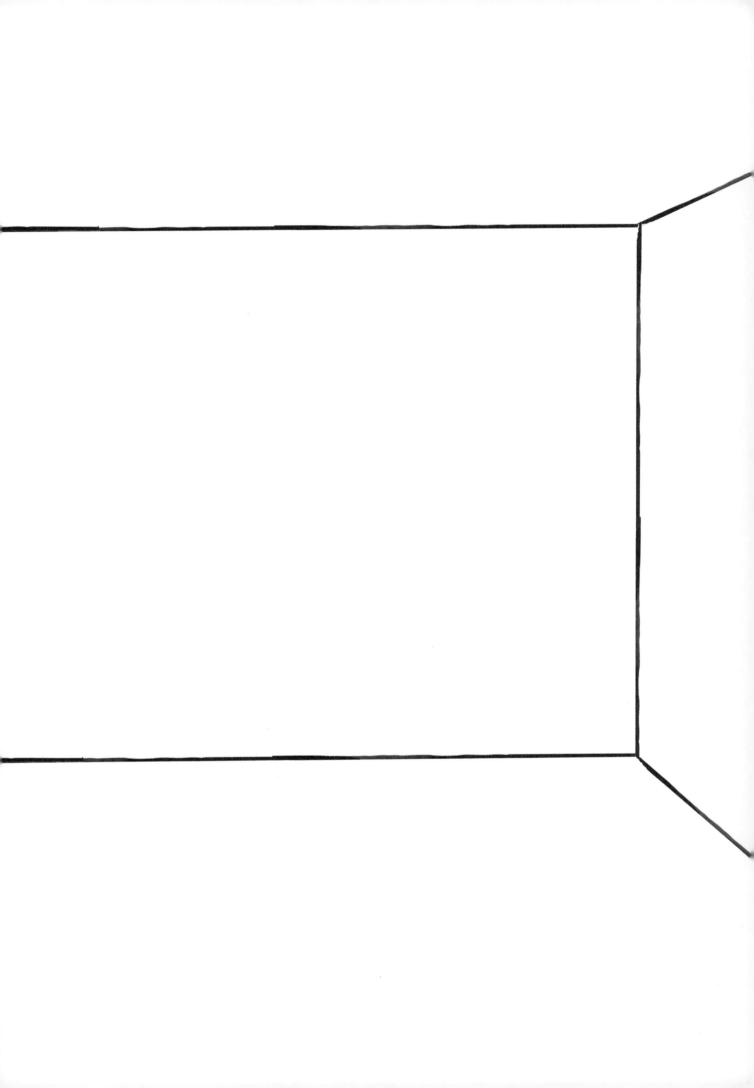

"TAKE AN OBJECT.

DO SOMETHING
to IT.

DO SOMETHING
ELSE to IT.

DO
SOMETHING
ELSE
to IT."

JASPER JOHNS

"THERE IS NOTHING UGLY IN ART
EXCEPt tHAt
WHICH IS WItHOUt CHARACtER,
tHAt IS to SAY, tHAt
WHICH OFFERS NO OUtER OR
INNER tRUtH."
AUGUStE RODIN

"I SEARCH FOR REALNESS,
THE REAL FEELING OF A SUBJECT,
ALL THE TEXTURE AROUND IT ..."

ANDREW WYETH

"I THINK HAVING LAND AND NOT RUINING IT IS THE MOST BEAUTIFUL ART THAT ANYBODY COULD EVER WANT TO OWN."

ANDY WARHOL

"AS PRACTICE
MAKES PERFECT,
I CANNOT BUT
MAKE PROGRESS;
EACH DRAWING ONE MAKES,
EACH STUDY ONE PAINTS,
IS A STEP FORWARD."

VINCENt VAN GOGH

"It is the eye of ignorance
that assigns a fixed
and unchangeable
colour to every
object; beware
of this stumbling block."

PAUL
GAUGUIN

"I OFTEN THINK THAT THE NIGHT IS MORE ALIVE AND MORE RICHLY COLOURED THAN THE DAY."

VINCENT VAN GOGH

"PICK A THEME
AND WORK It to
EXHAUSTION ...

LOVE

... THE SUBJECT MUST BE SOMETHING YOU TRULY LOVE OR TRULY HATE."

HATE

DOROTHEA LANGE

"IF YOU COULD SAY IT IN WORDS THERE WOULD BE NO REASON TO PAINT."

EDWARD HOPPER

"I HAVE HAD
tHREE MAStERS,
NATURE,
VELÁZQUEZ
AND
REMBRANDt."
FRANCISCO GOYA

"THE ONLY THING I KNOW IS THAT I PAINT BECAUSE I NEED TO, AND I PAINT ALWAYS WHATEVER PASSES THROUGH MY HEAD WITHOUT ANY OTHER CONSIDERATION."

FRIDA KAHLO

"HAVE NO FEAR OF PERFECTION — YOU'LL NEVER REACH IT."

SALVADOR DALÍ

"WHEN I PAINt, tHE SEA ROARS, tHE OtHERS SPLASH ABOUt IN tHE BATH."
SALVADOR DALÍ

"I WOULD LIKE SOME DAY to tRAP A MOMENt of LIFE IN Its FULL ...

"... VIOLENCE, ItS FULL BEAUTY. tHAt WOULD BE tHE ULtIMAtE PAINtING."

FRANCIS BACON

"SOME COLOURS RECONCILE THEMSELVES TO ONE ANOTHER, OTHERS JUST CLASH ..."

EDVARD MUNCH

"I NEVER
PAINt
DREAMS
OR
NIGHtMARES.
I PAINt
MY
OWN
REALItY."

FRIDA KAHLO

"BEAUTY IS EVERYWHERE, IN THE ARRANGEMENT OF YOUR POTS AND PANS, ON THE WHITE WALL OF YOUR KITCHEN, PERHAPS MORE THAN IN YOUR EIGHTEENTH-CENTURY SALON OR IN THE OFFICIAL MUSEUM."

FERNAND LÉGER

"IT IS ONLY BY DRAWING OFTEN, DRAWING EVERYTHING, DRAWING INCESSANTLY, THAT ONE FINE DAY YOU DISCOVER TO YOUR SURPRISE THAT YOU HAVE RENDERED SOMETHING IN ITS TRUE CHARACTER."

CAMILLE PISSARRO